Nell the Nebbish

The True Adventures of a Mensch in Hiding

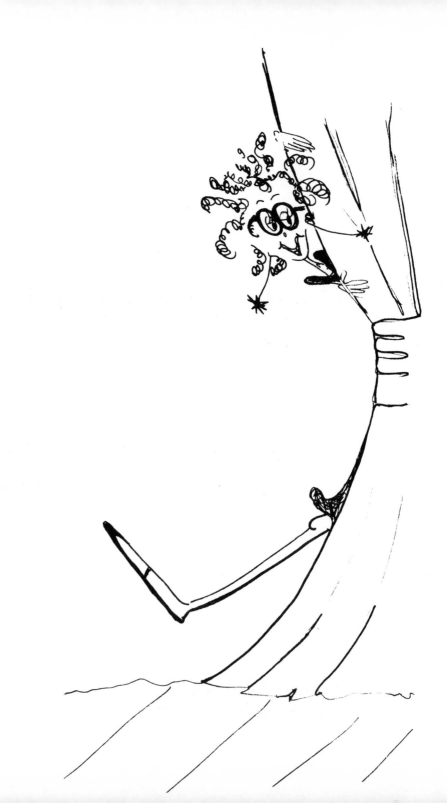

Nell the Nebbish*
The True Adventures of A Mensch** in Hiding

written by Rusty Berkus
illustrated by Esther Radom Pullan

RED ROSE
PRESS

*Nebbish: the undiscovered self
**Mensch: the magnificent self

Publisher's ISBN: 0-9609888-4-X

Printed in the United States of America by Delta Lithograph. Illustrations by Esther Radom Pullan. Typography by Deborah Spaulding, Ben Franklin Graphics. Edited by Alida Allison. Book designed by Mike Dirham. Consultation by Carolyn Geller. Epigraph illustration by Dr. Sandra Grifman.

Published by Red Rose Press
P.O. Box 24, Encino, California 91426
First Edition, First Printing, 1988

Other Books by Rusty Berkus

Life is a Gift
Appearances
To Heal Again
Soulprints

I celebrate myself and sing myself

—*Walt Whitman*

Glossary

Mensch: the magnificent self; the sunshine of the soul; the loving, spontaneous, courageous, honorable self.

Nebbish: the undiscovered self; the dark cloud of the soul; the helpless, self-pitying, impoverished, negative self.

Introduction

Once in a great while a person comes along whose view of reality works harmoniously with the universe. Such a person is Nell the Nebbish.

As Nell grew up, she did not fit into the American ideal of what a child is supposed to be like or look like. She was gangly, awkward, and did not excel in school or sports. Yet her parents had waited a decade for her arrival and viewed her as a treasure; they bestowed upon her unconditional love and acceptance. Thus Nell grew into womanhood thinking, feeling, and being in the world as if she were a "winner."

Nell is out there ready to get up time and time again. We applaud her, learn from her, and come to love her. We want her to make it, and there is no cause for concern. Nell knows there is no such thing as a final count because she can always count on herself.

Nell the Nebbish is about the sunshine of the soul. It celebrates the absence of oughts, shoulds and musts. It champions innocence, spontaneity, self-worth and love which dissolve all barriers.

Rusty Berkus

2

MY TYPE seems to be IN this year—
a tall,
skinny,
flat-chested,
frizzy-haired
forty-year-old
wearing braces.

I call it "funky chic."

3

4

I'M THE ONLY WOMAN I know
who has her mother over for dinner
every Friday night
and looks forward to it!

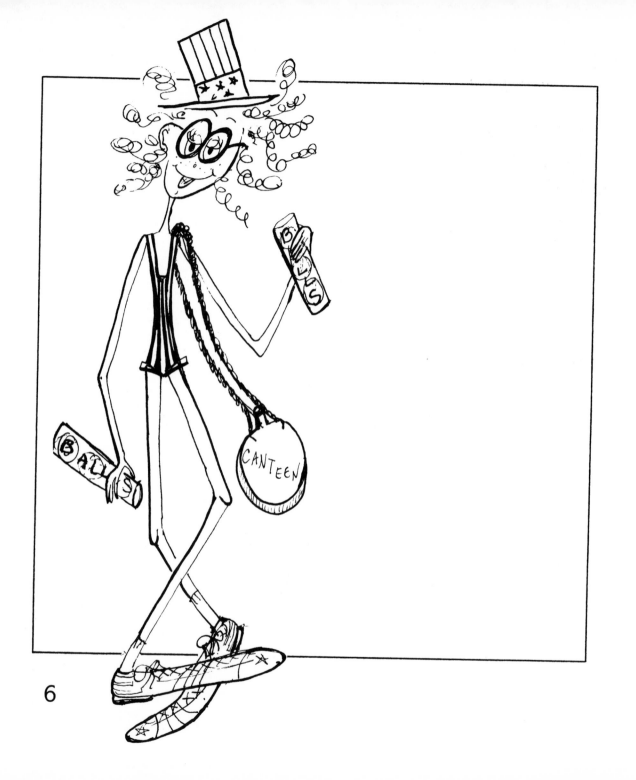

6

ON A JOB APPLICATION I was asked
to list my work experience.
The boss looked puzzled upon reading that I was
    the water girl on an archeological dig,
    the galley cook
    on a Jacques Cousteau expedition,
    ballgirl for Wimbledon,
    and president of the Goldie Hawn Fan Club.

I thought it would be obvious to anyone
that I am a woman for all seasons!

8

I WAS BEGINNING to wonder
why my Chinese fortune cookie always reads

"Better Luck Next Time."

Now I know what it means:

I always have something to look forward to!

9

10

I'M CONSTANTLY ASKED the same question:

Is Woody Allen your twin brother?

Of course I'm flattered
when people think
I'm related to such a respected creative person.

12

EVEN THOUGH I don't belong to the best clubs,
      didn't graduate from the finest schools,
      don't shop at elite boutiques,
and am not beautiful or famous yet,
I agree with my mother.

She says that any man who gets to know me
will adore me for my true self.

Mom says I'm gonna knock 'em dead—
all I need is EXPOSURE.

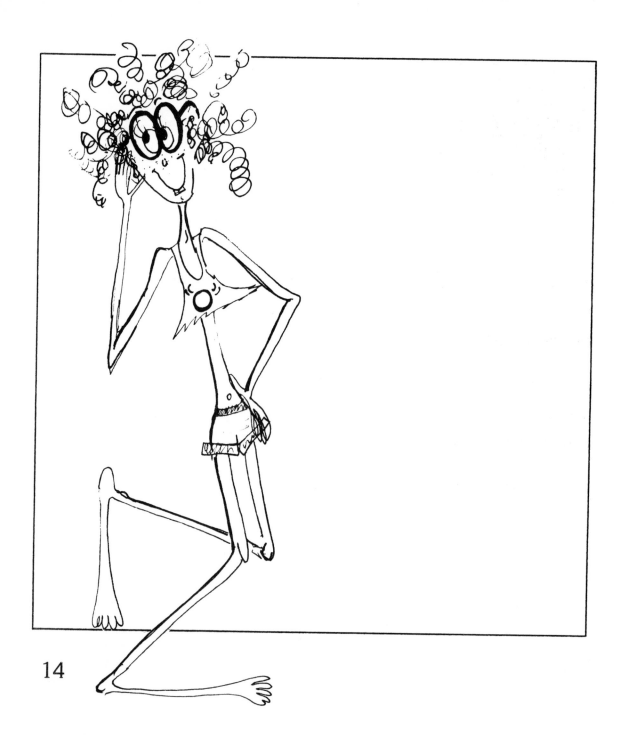

14

MY COUSIN MARVIN, the movie mogul, phoned
to say he wants me for his remake
of the movie "10."

Though I must admit "0" is a strange name
for a major motion picture,
I always knew Marvin would call.

Real talent wins out in the end!

16

I'M THE ONLY PERSON I know who
      owns no jogging suit or exercise machine,
      drives an old American economy car,
      has only one telephone and
      one black and white TV,
and who shops at Alpha Beta—with coupons.

My life style is so unique,
no wonder I never have
those identity crises everyone talks about.

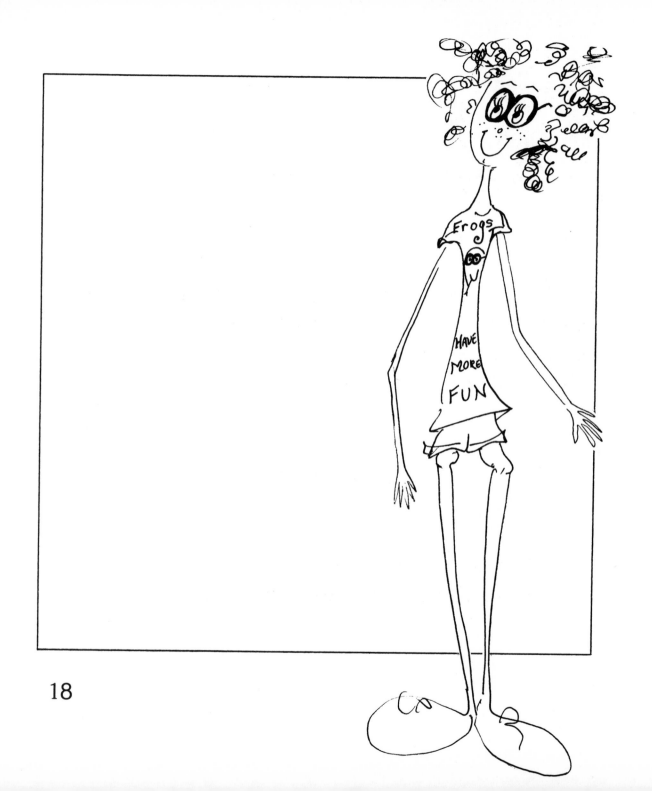

18

ALL MY GIRLFRIENDS get nightgowns and jewelry
for their birthdays. I can't understand why
I always get T-shirts
with strange messages on them, like—

      "Frogs have more fun"

or

      "Good Luck on Your Fortieth—
        You'll Need It."

or

      "It's okay to be single,
        even if it's for the rest of your life."

19

20

WHEN I WENT TO my 20th high school reunion,
I knew people might not
recognize me immediately.

But when they thought
I was one of their old teachers,
I felt sorry
that they had lapsed
into poor memory
at such a young and vital age.

22

AS A BIRTHDAY GIFT my friends hired an
astrologer to do my chart for the coming year.
He plotted the planets and had to admit
it was the first time he'd ever seen so many
lunar restrictions and negative aspects.
He gave me a rabbit's foot and a
gold four-leaf clover and told me
to stay in bed for the next six months.

Though it was nice of him to give me
such lovely gifts, I was surprised
he didn't know the big truth in the sky—

I affect my planets, they don't affect me!

24

EVERYONE SEEMS to have
      a therapist,
      guru,
      psychic
      or astrologer.

I talk directly to God.

You can't beat it
for low cost,
convenience
and results!

26

ON THE
　Minnesota
　　Multiphasic
　　　Diagnostic
　　　　Personality
　　　　　Inventory, they told me they were sorry to report the computer couldn't find a category for me.

I always knew I was one of a kind!

28

MY UNCLE, the famous doctor,
asked me what I thought
was the greatest killer
of people in our society today.

He looked aghast when I said:

> "That's very simple to answer,
>   Uncle Irving.
>   The greatest killer of people
>   is CRITICISM."

29

SWAMI SALAMI SAYS that through meditation
one's highest dreams can be realized;
all one need do is call in the energies.
I must have gotten
my metaphysical wires crossed
because all I have to report
is that twenty minutes later
I received my first obscene phone call!

32

THE DIVERSITY of my talent
is finally being recognized:
I've been asked to guest
on a TV talk show.

It's not "The Tonight Show,"
but I'm ecstatic I'll be on
the "Pre-Dawn Hour" which airs at 4 a.m.

Now everyone I know,
plus all those lucky insomniacs,
will get to hear what I have to say!

WHEN I WAITRESSED at the local diner,
everyone was impressed with the quality
of my service.

I couldn't bring myself to tell them
the secret of my success—
  in one of my past lives
  I was a queen
  waited on by hundreds of servants.

Therefore, I merely tapped into
cosmic memory to perfect my craft.

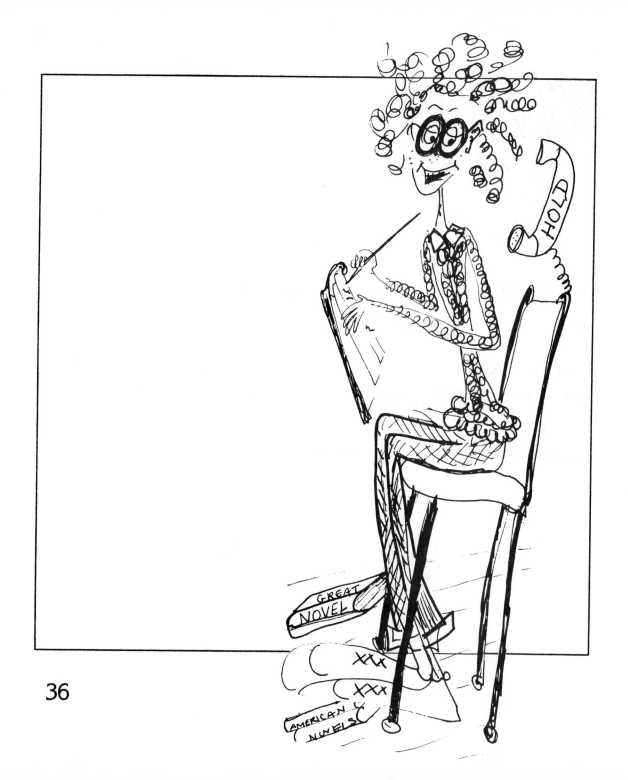

I'M PUT ON HOLD so much I decided
to use the time productively.

Within a week
I had written 892 pages
of what will probably be known
as the Great American Novel.

38

I SUSPECT that when I complete my new novel
about passion, lust, and intrigue,
everyone will assume
it's autobiographical.

People don't give me enough credit
for my fantastic imagination.

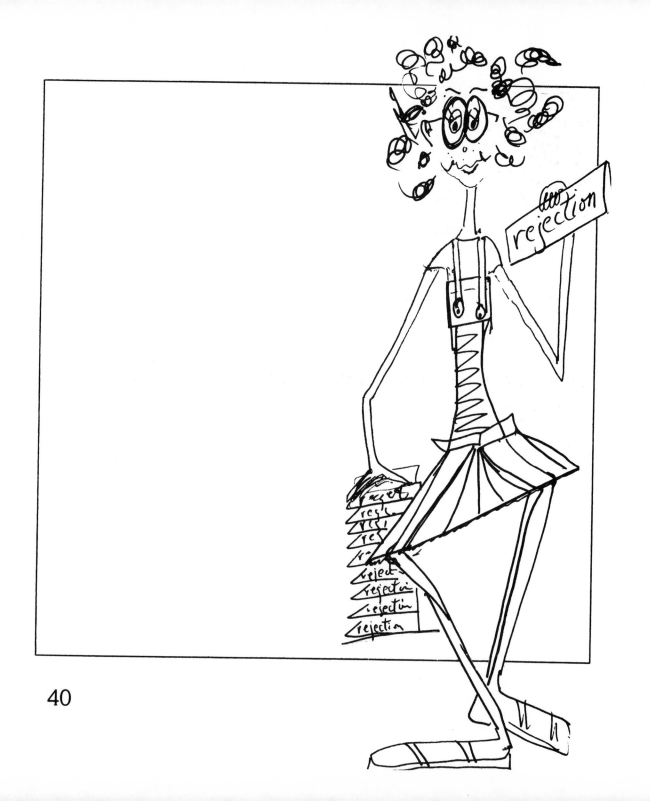

40

I GET SO MANY rejection slips I finally
started saving them.

Now I take them to the recycling center
and my writing
isn't a total loss.

42

NOW I KNOW HOW IT FEELS to be recognized
in the world of academia.

The Center for Research on Fragmentation
called to ask me to present a paper on
      "Everything You Wanted to Know
          about Failure,
          but Were Afraid to Ask."

No doubt you'll be able to look me up soon
in *Who's Who of American Women.*

I SUCCUMBED to advertising
and bought a telephone answering machine.

The other night I got a strange message:

"Nell, I can't stand it any longer.
No man has left a message on this machine.
I want you to hear me loud and clear.
I like you very much.
        This is Andrew,
        your friendly answering machine."

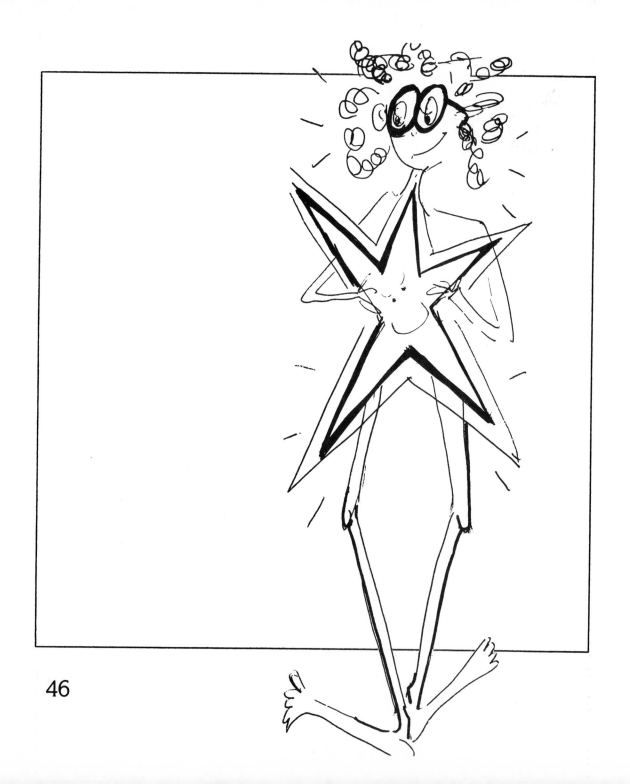

I'M USUALLY DESCRIBED as the kind of person
who would never inspire a fan club.

Most people don't know Star Quality
when it's twinkling
right before their eyes!

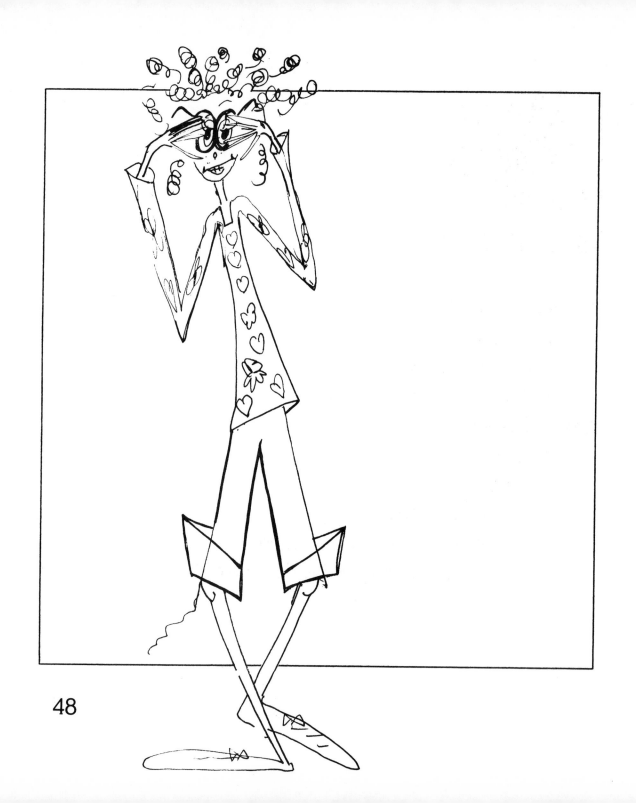

48

I KNOW FULL WELL
    behind these glasses,
    under this frizzy hair,
    within this buck tooth smile
lies a charismatic,
    sensual,
      creative,
        sophisticated,
          stable and loving person
            just waiting to be discovered!

"Ready or Not
Here I come."

To the divine in all of us—
Come out wherever you are.

THE SUN DOES NOT CHOOSE on whom to beam
its rays. It shines on all
who venture beneath the sky.

Nell the Nebbish symbolizes
the radiant self in all of us.

We need only acknowledge that it is there
in unlimited supply to tap into
our own magnificence—
　　　　our own Mensch in Hiding.

THE END